ANOREXIA NERVOSA AND THE WISH TO CHANGE

SELF-HELP AND DISCOVERY

THE THIRTY STEPS

Illustrations by Nicky Browne

The Self Help Series
from the
Department of Mental Health Sciences
St. George's Hospital Medical School
London

Published by

The Professorial Unit,
Division of General Psychiatry of the
Department of Mental Health Sciences,
St. George's Hospital Medical School,
Tooting, London SW17 0RE, U.K.

Tel: 01-672-9944 Ext. 55513

©1989   Department of Mental Health Sciences,
          St. George's Hospital Medical School.

ISBN   0 9515431 0 5

This booklet can be purchased from
the above address or from the
Eating Disorders Association,
Sackville Place, 44-48 Magdalen
Street, Norwich NR3 1JE.

Proceeds from the sale of this booklet
go to the Psychiatry Fund of the
St. George's Hospital Special
Trustees and any surplus will be
used to finance research into
anorexia nervosa.

ACKNOWLEDGEMENTS

We should like to express our thanks to our patients, who are also our friends and who have taught us so much about this illness and how sometimes to recover from it.

We should also like to thank Nicky Browne for her skillful illustrations, some of which were based on feelings expressed pictorially by patients; and Heather Humphrey for somehow steering the manuscript through a dozen drafts.

The authors are employed
at St. George's Hospital and
Medical School, London.

A.H. Crisp is Professor of Psychiatry;
Neil Joughin is Lecturer in Psychiatry;
Chris Halek is Nurse Specialist;
Carol Bowyer is Senior Dietician.

Let me be

CONTENTS

Page

Foreword 1

WHAT IS ANOREXIA NERVOSA?
Our view and messages 3

Hello 3
Why do people have anorexia nervosa? 5
Coming to terms with the idea
    of having anorexia nervosa 8
The costs of anorexia nervosa 10
Males with anorexia nervosa 11
A message to parents 13
A message to spouses/partners 15

HOW TO CHANGE: THE 30 STEPS 17

What happens if you try
    to give up anorexia? 17
How to find out
    what underlies your anorexia 18
How to stop losing weight 24
How to try to recover 28
How to gain weight 32
How to live at a normal weight 34
If you can't get back to a normal weight 37

Page

WORK SECTION 39

EXPLORATORY EXERCISES

Effects of weight gain in anorexia nervosa 41
Draw a 'life-map' 46
Make a weight biography 47
Draw a family tree 48
Plot your family relationships 50
Draw your family sitting in a circle 51
Imagine how other members of
    your family would describe you 52

ON-GOING EXERCISE

Keeping a diary 53
Keeping a logbook 55
Keeping a weight chart 60

PRACTICAL INFORMATION SECTION 61

Energy balance 62
Changing your behaviour 76
Weight tables 83
Professional help 88
Useful addresses 95
Reading list 97

FOREWORD

There are very few specialist services for those affected with the so-called "eating disorders". Of course, it isn't only specialists who can help and it certainly is the case that specialists cannot always help. You may know only too well how difficult it is to change, with or without outside help. Moreover, those few specialist resources that exist in the UK are being increasingly restricted by managerial decisions to providing local or sub-regional services. Even so, they remain overwhelmed with referrals of would-be patients, and often can't accept them all. This is despite the reluctance of many of those afflicted even to seek the possibility of such help or to agree to it being sought for them! So who can help? Can self-help work?

Self-help is a complicated concept. To the authors it does not necessarily mean seeking to help oneself in isolation from professional helpers or from the family. That attitude may be unconstructive and indeed characterises part of the problem underlying the disorder. Rather, the authors see self-help as meaning that the person with the problem is committed to change to a better kind of self-regulation and to shrugging off the disorder if at all possible. That preliminary step may itself open the door to such change. Then you can hopefully begin to search for possible support in the task. Mutual support can derive from contact with fellow sufferers, especially if they are also motivated to change. You could also hope that so-called experts and people themselves not afflicted (perhaps including your own family) might be available to take your hand, open doors and point the way. Of course, when it comes to anorexia nervosa, your family may need such help alongside you but this doesn't mean that you may not also be able to help each other if you decide to try.

This booklet confines itself to consideration of anorexia nervosa within the above framework. It complements the first author's views contained in more detail in his book, *Anorexia Nervosa: Let Me Be*, referred to in the text.

The aim of this booklet is to try to help you help yourself.

WHAT IS ANOREXIA NERVOSA?
Our View and our Messages

We are our parents and their bond;
please let us be fulfilled.

Hello

We want you to think carefully before you decide to give up anorexia. The chances are that a lot of people have told you that you will feel better if you gain weight. This may be true in the long term, but you know only too well that it isn't in the short term.

It may be that you don't feel you have anorexia. Some books or films offer a particular picture of the problem. For instance some people will say that they haven't got the disorder because they don't binge and vomit, as they saw happening in the film *Catherine*. These aren't necessary symptoms. More often the problem is in accepting the implications of the label of anorexia nervosa. You may fear that you will then be regarded as no more than an "anorectic" or else "just an awkward girl who refuses to eat". You may feel you would be more exposed to people offering you advice or threats about the need to eat. You, and your family, would have to face the fact that there is a serious problem, which at best results in a limited life, at worst can result in death. It is easy to see why "anorectic" is a hard label to accept.

This booklet has to deal with anorexia in general. It will therefore be easy to be critical of those aspects which are "not about me", and therefore ignore all the advice. This is your choice, but we think you should seriously consider the possibility that someone else is able to understand you - even if this hasn't been your recent experience.

Why do people have anorexia?

Because they are overweight? This explanation is far too simple. You felt fat and overweight - but why? The majority of people have their first episodes of anorexia in their teens, and women who never develop anorexia often feel uncomfortable especially during their teens with their newly acquired body shape, wish they were thinner and diet intermittently. Very few people find adolescence and its tasks of forging an adult personality easy. It is a time of challenges. It starts, several years before the first menstruation in females, at the onset of puberty with those very changes in body shape due to body fat about which many young women, and some young men, become sensitive. These concerns can get powerfully attached in your mind to the other new experiences which come with puberty, and which, in one way or another, have become frightening for you. The end of adolescence is more difficult to identify. Adolescent problems can be reactivated later in life, for instance at the time of marriage, childbirth or death of a parent, and such events can then cause an episode of anorexia nervosa later in life. The assumption that an eighteenth or twenty first birthday marks our readiness for adulthood does not always reflect reality.

Anorexia nervosa is an unwitting reversal and thereafter an avoidance of development. It can be understood as a way of banishing insecurity and conflict, often including conflict or potential conflict between you and your family. Weight loss and loss of

5

plumpness returns your body and its feelings to its state before puberty. Symbolically enough, if you are female, your periods stop early on or your development may arrest even before your periods have started and many of the problems of adulthood come to be completely avoided. Thus weight loss works even more effectively than a tranquillising drug or alcohol. The emotions that have been most hard to tolerate are dampened down and eliminated and a kind of security achieved. Within your state of starvation, distress is channelled exclusively into panic about losing control of your low body weight - a price you have obviously needed to pay.

Many people ask whether something to do with sex is at the bottom of the problem. The answer is yes and no. Sex is an inescapable aspect of growth into an adult. It is the product of puberty and relates to the sensitivity that many females and males develop at this stage about their bodies - with females being more concerned about their "fatness". Many people also ask whether anorexia nervosa is caused by previous sexual abuse. Such abuse has sometimes occurred in the backgrounds of those with anorexia nervosa. When this is the case it is invariably a most important influence on the condition. It can leave the affected person very fearful of their development or even deadened. But intense fear of sexuality can have many other origins. For instance sexuality may threaten a family which is too tightly bound up in itself or too distanced from the various values of the outside world which beckons the adolescent, or where parents' love is too conditional on compliance, or the family too committed to furthering your social or educational development above everything else. Then again, children may see one of their parents apparently damaged by the sexual conduct of the other parent, may even fear being like the latter parent themselves and thus cause further harm. Sex may become "bad" and relief from its impulse profound, and an especially close bond may become forged with the "damaged" parent. Such complete reversion to "childhood" as anorexia nervosa reflects may also re-cement some parental marriages which need the presence of the child in the family for their survival. As puberty develops and adolescence arises, sex can rarely be denied and becomes a major factor of either a real or imagined kind in relationships with people of your own age. If you are to feel secure in the outside world you will need to have worked out a personal solution rather than an imposed one to this dilemma. We prefer to view sex as a powerful and inescapable force but equally aim to put it in its place when trying to understand its influence. Sex in our view is best seen in terms of other human needs for love, security, respect, self-esteem, self-control, immortality, and the usual human search for intimacy that links these things. This applies not only to you but to those around you including your parents. If sex has got out of hand - becoming too stifled or too unmanageable - then an underlying question concerns what other needs are not being met.

People also sometimes ask whether anorexia nervosa is inherited. Many disorders are a product of both inheritance and development and this is true for anorexia nervosa. We touch on this in the section addressed to parents.

Coming to terms with the idea of having anorexia nervosa

As mentioned above, there is a variety of reasons for not accepting the idea that you are suffering from anorexia nervosa. It perhaps becomes a more acceptable idea if you understand the problem in a broader context than eating behaviour, and if you are clear that it is a major problem that warrants help rather than scorn or dismissal from others. Anorexia nervosa is often called an eating disorder as if this was its primary basis, and of course eating is severely disordered in it, and this may be causing great problems in the family. For instance, if your family is together then you may notice that your mother now appears to feel helpless and your father perhaps angry and helpless. However, it is our belief that the (hidden) psychological problem revolves importantly around the meaning of body shape and hence weight, and this is what you need to understand. This understanding will need to link your shape and weight with problems in your development, usually involving you and your family, which we believe underwrite the condition. They may or may not have been acknowledged at the time. Present family relationships and strains are different and will not reflect the problem that existed before your anorexia nervosa developed.

You are likely to have anorexia nervosa if you have a (secret) terror of being more than about 7 stones*; less if the onset was very early in your life or you are especially short, or perhaps rather more if you are male and taller. For you, your weight is indeed the be all and end all of "being". As a result of your terror, you keep your weight down, and this results in a state of chronic bodily starvation hedged around by defences against weight gain to the exclusion of everything else.

---

* A *stone* is a unit of weight familiar to people in the UK. There are 14 lbs in 1 stone and 2.2lbs in 1kg. ☛ *Detailed conversions between these three measures are laid out on pp. 86-87.*

You may have got used to defiantly claiming that your condition is fulfilling, but you may in fact experience it more as a vitally necessary safe, or not so safe, retreat. This is the trap of anorexia nervosa. You are caught within a distressing way of life, but if you share your fears with other people you find, or fear, that they will not understand. You therefore say that you are "fine". You will be used to creating such smokescreens: convincing other people that you are puzzled as to why you don't gain weight, claiming that you can at last crack it by yourself, gaining a little weight at the cost of great anxiety in order to reassure others, denying to others your all-absorbing preoccupations. You must shed such defences. They simply distance you even more from those around you. Accepting and acknowledging the idea of anorexia nervosa is necessary if you are going to tackle the problem.

The costs of anorexia nervosa

Others will not always share your apparent ease with your situation and will try to interfere. For you yourself, as the condition progresses, the costs become more evident. Anorexia is a full-time job. Your preoccupation with food prevents other activities. Friends sense that something is wrong and back away. You fail to tackle difficult emotions that would have been prompted by your adult body including its sexuality: for instance in learning to cope in relationships with people of your own age and in renegotiating your relationship with your parents.

Those people who remain in contact may do so in response to you as an invalid, not for love of the adult you. Life leaves you behind. Sometimes this realisation happens many years after the onset of the problem, leaving an awful feeling that it is too late to catch up.

1

Males with anorexia nervosa

If you are a male with anorexia nervosa and have been reading this you may by now feel baffled and worried. How do many of the features which seem to be specifically female relate to your own problem? Is there something especially wrong with you since the condition is so rare amongst males?

The answer is that a great deal of what has been written applies to you. Loss of periods in the female is part of the early response to reduced energy intake (energy rich food) affecting reproductive and sexual behaviour and feelings in general which is equally mirrored in you. The question is the same - what is behind this process? The answers, we suggest, are also the same and reflected in the general content and the 30 STEPS presented in this booklet.

Males are less often concerned about their "fatness" than females but this can arise if you have been definitely fat and teased or else, sometimes, if you have been experiencing some doubt and panic about, say, your masculinity. Such gender doubt during adolescence is not uncommon and also arises amongst females, but may be less conspicuous.

As with females, we are able to tell you that it is very definitely possible to recover from anorexia nervosa and, in our view, you can best take the same steps to try to achieve this - all 30 of them!

A message to parents

If you are involved as parents you will probably feel
helpless and very anxious. You will wonder whether
you are to "blame" and whether there may still be
some manoeuvre that will help your child to gain
weight.

Blame is not, in our view, the right concept; nor is it
a creative one. We do believe you are very importantly
involved. You and your children find yourselves with
inherited characteristics. These can contribute to
anorexia nervosa. They may have to do with your
shapes, your relationships with food, a tendency to
deal with strains by avoiding them, a particular mode
of thinking, feelings of anxiety and low self-esteem.
Such characteristics can probably sometimes be
modified or kept at bay. More important may be the
ways of dealing with problems that you have
developed and the nature of your relationship as a
couple. Some marriages are held together by children.
Other parents are insulated from the outside world,
requiring this also of their children. Such conditional
acceptance can place impossible strain on sensitive
young adults who need to forge a link between
parental values and those of the outside world.
Remember, our children can help us keep in touch
with an ever rapidly changing world! Have you
shared your own fears and backgrounds, including
your own teenage years, with them or indeed with
each other? Looking again at your teens, how did you
really cope and could you have done it better and less
defensively? Be honest and then you may have the
strength to help your anorectic child. It is easy to

have misjudged your child's needs prior to the onset of the disorder. Other patterns and strains can arise within anorectic families and are touched on earlier in this booklet and also, in greater detail, in *Anorexia Nervosa: Let Me Be* (☞ *see Reading List p.97).*

The booklet is intended for you as well as the family member with anorexia nervosa. You can have a vital role helping the anorectic to recover. Without your involvement the anorectic is more likely to feel, paradoxically it may seem, that she is betraying you if she gains weight. At the same time you may sense her anger at the situation she finds herself in. The booklet is intended to help sufferers understand their own anorexia and hence achieve change. This is much more possible if those around the sufferer are also able to understand the anorectic predicament and their part within this. They can thus offer support and perhaps also change. Involvement with your child does NOT mean dictating that she or he eat the kind of diet discussed, but may mean offering to provide the kind of diet discussed, and helping the anorectic to reconstruct what was happening in their lives when eating problems began. For this to be done effectively the anorectic will need your permission at the very least. Even if you have anorexia yourself, or some other major problem, e.g. a drink problem, then perhaps now is the time to acknowledge it.

These ideas can be hard to understand. When you are living with the chaos, distress or despair that anorexia nervosa can provoke and feeling that you don't know what to do, it is difficult to concentrate on these concepts. All you can think about is the next meal, and survive day to day. To think back to the past may seem irrelevant, indulgent or perhaps distressing. However it is necessary. If you do not understand how important families can be, and how they influence people, we strongly recommend a book *Families and How to Survive Them (☞ see Reading List, p.100)*. Remember, your anorectic child is being advised in this book to look at her or his childhood background. Perhaps you should have another look at your own childhood and adolescence. It may be painful but it may help you to recognise and identify with the present underlying problems.

A message to spouses/partners

A lot may depend on whether you married your partner before or after the development of her or his condition. You may need to reflect that the anorexia is an important requirement of the marriage. If you now want to help your partner throw it off then you will certainly need to get involved with the tasks that we have outlined here and almost certainly you will need to change yourself rather more substantially than might naturally occur. The same things apply if you are an established partner though not married.

HOW TO CHANGE:
THE 30 STEPS

What happens if you try
to give up anorexia?

Attempts to give up anorexia through gaining weight result first of all in intensified panic about your weight. If you gain more weight you may experience once again those earlier frightening and unpleasant feelings of which you had rid yourself and which have been touched on above. Yet those around you look more cheerful, as they see reassuring evidence that you are gaining weight and hope or conclude that the problem is resolved. You yourself, however, feel emotionally much worse, and often angry at others' failure to realise what you are going through. Too easily this becomes a good and necessary reason for once again retreating into weight loss. You will find lists at the end of this booklet of the possible effects of gaining weight up to adult levels and also, by implication, of losing weight down to anorectic levels (☞ *pp.42-45*). Later on we shall be inviting you to consider those lists in terms of yourself.

How to find out
what underlies your anorexia
(STEPS 1 - 9)

Whether your aim at the present time is to escape from the grip of anorexia or to be a better adapted anorectic, you are unlikely to be able to achieve these things if you only address your eating problem and fail to recognise and come to terms, at least to some extent, with the underlying issues affecting your fear of gaining weight to a normal adult level. The following is a series of steps that we hope might help you in this latter task. Remember that, emotionally, you are certainly no older than the year that this condition developed and that you may always have been young for your age (although others may have seen you as particularly mature, perhaps because you were "good" within the more structured environment of home or school). *Begin now to use your diary (☞ p. 53) to record your journey up these first nine steps.*

STEP 1.

> Stop and think.
> Could it be that your illness is helping you and others to avoid the strains of life? Remember that those strains will no longer be present - the anorexia nervosa has solved them (but brought others). ☞ *Go to the Effects of Weight Gain exercise (pp.42-45)* and try to complete it in relation to your own situation.

STEP 2.

> Ask yourself - should I stop in my tracks now and try to unscramble things before any more time is lost?
> You've given up any faith that you had in other people understanding you. You can accept this or you can try again. How can you make it different next time?

STEP 3.

> Try and reflect who you might be if you were not
> now an anorectic.
> Reflect on what was happening around the time
> that you became self-conscious about your shape
> and began to do something about it.

Perhaps your anorexia nervosa has allowed you to
preserve (or recreate) an earlier pattern of
relationships and behaviour which had come to be
threatened, although this may now be swamped in
many ways by the new conflict over you not
eating. You see, the anorexia doesn't work very
well, does it? Think of it in terms of yourself and
your position in the family even if you are
chronologically in your twenties or thirties, or
even older now.

STEP 4.

> Start getting to know yourself better. In the first
> instance tackle the Exploratory Exercises in the
> Work Section of this booklet.

STEP 5.

> Start communicating better with your parents so
> far as this is possible. Everyone has important
> aspects of their parents within them. In learning
> about them you will learn about yourself,
> including the different parts of yourself that may
> not be communicating well with each other!
> Remember your parents are in the same position

as you. They may also need to communicate better within themselves and with each other. They are children of their parents. If possible ask your parents about their own adolescence. Do the Exploratory Exercises with them and talk about relevant feelings. You will not begin to find yourself until you have found them.

To learn to communicate requires opportunity and practice.

STEP 6.

Therefore, use your friends, e.g. by going out with them. Try to think about this in a new way. Instead of panicking or regretting it, ask why you might be avoiding doing it.

Like many other avoidance mechanisms, anorexia nervosa can exist in the background of anorectics and their families. Other strategies include avoiding communication, avoiding social contact, dependence on alcohol and withdrawing into depression. Anorexia nervosa itself can run in families.

STEP 7.

Recognise and acknowledge that your anorexia stifles unpleasant feelings i.e. protects you from such feelings through the effects of your low weight. Remember you are an expert in anorexia nervosa. What you need to do is to develop new skills.

STEP 8.

> You will need to begin to tolerate feeling bad and frightened. This is true for many of us but especially for you.

STEP 9.

> Be truthful. Do not deceive yourself even if you still have to deceive others occasionally. Beware of excuses - the reasons you will think of for not acting now will probably be quite varied. Who are you trying to fool?

☞ *We suggest you take some time now to think about what you have learnt from these steps. You will need eventually to make a decision about where to go from here. Do not rush into attempts to recover unless you have considered the implications and you have the necessary resources around you. Timing is very important. When you feel you are ready to make a decision you have several options. Firstly, if you are still losing weight, you will need to stop doing so. Then you will need to decide whether to try and hold that position temporarily, or to aim for recovery, or to remain an anorectic in the long term. Remember that you are making a decision for the time being - it may be that you need longer to think about things, or do not have the necessary resources available to you. You can always make a new decision at another time, but it is probably true that the longer you live within anorexia the harder it is to recover. First of all you may need to learn how to stop losing more weight.*

How to stop losing weight - (STEPS 10 - 15)

STEP 10.

Consider your weight. Below 7 stones or there-abouts depending on height, anorectics feel safer but there is no great psychological need to go down very much lower if only you could be confident of steadying your weight at just below this level. Of course this is an unnatural task for your body. The great thrust in it is to grow and to develop, and to develop other impulses than simply the one to eat. It is these other potential impulses (such as the sexual impulse and the body's push to explore and assert itself) that are compounding your fear about consuming more "fuel" and gaining more weight, and lead to your fear of losing control of yourself. They underwrite your sense of incompetence and low self-esteem and feeling that you do not own your body. They may have been reduced to the impulse to eat but will intensify that because it is basically safer. However, if you surrender to it you still get very distressed because you recognise your continuing poor self-control and this is now declared in terms of your "fatness", with its sexual meanings. If you are going to recover from your condition you will need to accept your sexuality and come to feel confident with it, but that can only happen gradually. You will also need to cope with its consequences. This may include the need to learn to separate yourself more from your parents, to work out a new relationship with them and to develop your personal identity. Your anorexia will have been triggered by such challenges in the first instance.

24

STEP 11.

> Having got this far perhaps you can now begin to allow yourself to think about your eating in terms of changing it to stablilise your low weight in the first instance.

STEP 12.

> Some people who have anorexia nervosa simply restrict their diet but others binge as well as cutting down on food. You may do this yourself. (By "bingeing" we mean consuming large amounts of food, not eating a little more than you had planned, which some anorectics feel is bingeing.) Your bingeing is reinforced by your low weight and inadequate and irregular food intake. For instance, your body reacts to starvation with increased preoccupation with food and hunger, and if you cannot resist this, then a binge may follow. You may feel as though your control has "snapped", and you then over-compensate by eating as much as possible, usually of the foods which you have been avoiding (carbohydrates including sweet foods). You will know how distressing and frightening this experience is and that it is usually followed by vomiting to prevent weight gain. We believe that it is almost impossible to stop bingeing unless you eat regularly throughout the day rather than, say, refrain from eating during the main part of it. Your diet must therefore include some carbohydrate at every meal every day.

2

25

STEP 13.

So, whether you occasionally binge, or binge and vomit, or mainly restrict your diet, you are more likely to achieve stability of your present weight in the first instance if you eat several times each day and, as has already been said and as we now repeat, you must consume a reasonable number of calories on these occasions. You may well be a great expert in the identification of calories in food. To maintain your present weight you should consume 1000-1500 calories per day (*see p.69)*, depending on your height and maturity (*see Weight Table, pp.84-85)*, and of course not vomit, use laxatives, or exercise endlessly.

STEP 14.

If you have been habitually vomiting or using laxatives, you need to wean yourself off this behaviour. People find that different approaches help in different circumstances. Vomiting and using laxatives seriously upset the chemistry in your body and in that sense you will feel somewhat better when you stop. Using laxatives is also a desperate manoeuvre since it mainly gets rid of fluid and renders you unable to drink even water without your body clinging on to it and increasing your weight. Some people can simply stop these behaviours and others tail them off, and now is the time for you to do one or other of these things *(see Changing your behaviour, p.76)*.

STEP 15.

You will also need to tackle the problems of any excessive exercise that you have been taking. A certain amount of exercise is natural for human beings but you will know, if you are honest with yourself, whether yours is excessive, and if so you should now reduce this to normal levels as best you can, although we know your starving condition itself will probably be making you restless.

In the Work Section we suggest some guidelines which may help you change such behaviours as bingeing, vomiting, laxative abuse and excessive exercise, provided you are simultaneously working through the first nine steps.

If you are planning to stay an anorectic and simply improve your condition within it as far as possible then all that has so far been said can be of help but you should skip the next section and move on to the section starting on page 37.

2

How to try to recover - (STEPS 16 - 21)

(i.e. gain weight to an
adult level and cope with
its consequences.)

If you would like to recover from the disorder then
you are going to need, sooner or later, **to begin to
grow in every sense**. You may need permission for
this, so seek it e.g. from your family and from
yourself, and growth should happen slowly. You may
also need help from others including professionals
and so consider seeking that also. If your parents or
partner can also change then this will help; much of
what we are saying applies equally to them.

STEP 16.

> Remember once again that, emotionally, you are
> certainly no older than the year that this condition
> developed and that you may always have been
> emotionally young for your age.

STEP 17.

> Give yourself time.

STEP 18.

> Start using your logbook now (☛ *see pp.55-59)*.
> Study it and use it from now on.

STEP 19.

You will need to learn about your physical self. This includes discovering that you own and are responsible for your complete and adult body, and its energy. When you eventually gain weight above that 7 stone level it also means coming to terms with your inevitable physical sexual redevelopment, and indeed eventually coming to enjoy its potential. Incidentally, we think it is very important when you reach a normal weight, that you avoid pregnancy for at least the next year or two whilst you continue to discover and develop yourself.

STEP 20.

You will have to come to terms with your parents, not only in how you relate to them as people, but also in how you relate to them inside you. This involves renegotiating your relationship with them so that you can be separate from them, but also respected and loved for yourself.

STEP 21.

You need to develop a general sense of your own competence. This can come from engaging in the tasks outlined in the steps, rather than depending totally on your being a successful anorectic. If you cannot achieve all the ideal goals outlined here, then doing your best is just as important.

2

☛ *Now go back and reconsider STEPS 1 - 9 as the possible means of achieving this along with the following steps, and remember that none of the above tasks can be fully completed unless you gain weight - because this makes the emotions real rather than theoretical.*

How to gain weight - (STEPS 22 - 26)

STEP 22.

Set yourself a "target weight". Your target weight should be the weight of the average person in our population of your height and sex and, we suggest, of the age that you fell ill (☞ *see pp.84-85)*. We recommend this since it is at this age, emotionally speaking, that you need to pick up life again.

STEP 23.

Once again, you are more likely to find gaining weight easier if you eat several times each day and consume a reasonable number of calories on each occasion. You will need to build up to an amount which will lead to weight gain in the context of normal but not excessive exercise. For the moment you should walk no more than two to three miles per day at the most and not engage in other contrived exercise. Your calorie needs are determined to an important extent by your present weight and height and you will need to slowly increase your present calorie intake. ☞ *We recommend you do this in a controlled, precise way as we have outlined on pages 67-70.* You will need to persevere with the tasks of controlling any bingeing, vomiting and laxative abuse.

STEP 24.

An almost universal fear is that if you relax your
retrictions on diet you will gain weight rapidly
and then not stop. You therefore need to weigh
yourself weekly - more often may give you
misleading information, and weighing yourself too
often is probably a symptom of your anorexia. Plot
your measured weight (don't cheat) on a chart
☛ *(see Keeping a Weight Chart, p.60)*. We would
recommend a weight gain of about 1 lb (0.5 kg)
per week. Less than this can be hard to monitor.
More is likely to outstrip the changes that we
think you need to make in parallel with gaining
weight - you may then panic and rebound into
losing weight.

If you have been vomiting, using laxatives or
restricting how much fluid you drink then you will
be dehydrated. Therefore, if you give up these
behaviours you may well initially gain weight
more quickly than 1 lb a week. This will mean you
are "rehydrating" (taking water back into your
body to bring it back to normal). This is not the
same as gaining weight through eating, but can be
equally terrifying. The rate of weight gain will not
continue once you have "rehydrated" - the process
will take a couple of weeks to stabilise (if you give
up vomiting etc. completely).

2

STEP 25.

> Do not let people/parents tempt you to eat too much. It will be a long while before you can take control for granted.

STEP 26.

> Most people with anorexia fear that once they start gaining weight they will not be able to stop. Having reached your "target weight" it is very important that you stop gaining. Gain much more and you are certain to panic and probably feel the need to resort to a low weight again. ☛ *In the Dietary Plans section (p.67)* we offer advice about how to level-off your weight. However, being at a normal weight is only the start.

How to live at a normal weight - (STEPS 27-30)

STEP 27.

> Recognise that you cannot immediately stop having many anorectic attitudes once you get to a normal weight. On the contrary, they may be intense and only wither slowly, but we are now asking you to live with them and not lose weight. Thus a lot of other things have to change along with your weight such as those listed in the

important STEPS 19-21. Keep going back over these together with your family or by yourself if you have to. Such issues are fundamental to your condition and to the possibilities for change. Progress can arise as you gradually expose your body and yourself to the realities of your problems and discover how to cope by completing the 30 STEPS. It is best if you try to change these things slowly, and recognise that the time scale must be months or years. There are no short cuts to recovering from anorexia nervosa.

STEP 28.

Living at a normal weight is the hardest stage of all. You have begun to give up one identity, and probably not yet found another. You are exposed to feelings that have proved unbearable in the past, and others may be thinking that you are "cured". It is your job to help them understand how you feel, to explain how appearing physically better is not the same as feeling better.

STEP 29.

Remember that humanity is made up of a rich diversity of people. No one is perfect and many of us are far from perfect. If we have all been importantly influenced by our environment then blame is not a useful concept at this stage for you or, for instance, your parents. You undoubtedly need at least one friend or other such person whom you can trust and with whom and through whom you can continue to grow. You cannot expect such a person, if indeed they are going to be strong enough to help you, to meet your every felt need at this stage. Indeed, do not rush into commitments. As we have said before, give yourself a year or two after getting your weight back. Remember you have some catching up to do first in discovering who you are.

STEP 30.

Allow others to help you. As we have said, living at a normal weight is the hardest stage of all. It is now that you will need extra support to help you cope with those things that your anorexia has enabled you to avoid in the past. While this support may be available to you within your family or circle of friends, or a self-help group, it is probably worth considering allowing a professional therapist to help you at this stage. Remember, you do not have to be underweight or eating abnormally to ask for help. Help may be available from many sources. (☛ *see Practical Information section, p.88)* If you do not hit it off with the first person you see, don't assume no-one can help, try again. It's worth it. You are worth it.

If you can't get back to a normal weight

This can happen for a number of reasons, but most often because you are unable to obtain, or accept, the support that is necessary to weather the storms of living at a normal weight. There may be an alternative. The alternative is to try to live with long-term controlled anorexia; maintaining a weight that isn't life threatening. ☛ *You may find it useful at this stage to go back to STEPS 10-15.* Consume a structured diet that minimises the risks of your eating developing into a pattern of chaos - binges, vomiting and fasting (☛ *using Eating plan A, p.73, until you have gained weight to about 6 $^1/_2$ - 7 stones and thereafter Eating plan B).* Find structured social outlets, such as part-time employment, to maintain contact with the outside world. Try to use this booklet in ways which you think are relevant to you and do some of the exercises. It may be possible for you to make limited changes that will improve things for you without your having to give up your anorexia.

This alternative has a price. Personal relationships with other people will never be normal, achievements in work are likely to be limited, and you will be faced with chronic preoccupations with food that will dominate your life. Meanwhile, try to keep in touch with others even if you can only manage those relationships which are socially structured rather than personal and intimate. Life may well get easier for you as you approach middle age and, indeed, later recovery remains a possibility, although the longer you leave it the more difficult it is fully to escape its grip.

2

Each of the steps contains at least one particular thing for you to do; some contain several that are very important! Now that you have read this through for the first time go on and read the rest of the booklet. Then if you decide to try to recover, go through the steps and identify and underline each point. As you take the steps use the margins on each page to note things down (successes and temporary failures) as well as making sure that you use the work section to your best advantage.

GOOD LUCK to you all.

Remember there is one great sportsman who, accused of being lucky, is said to have replied:

"The harder I practice, the luckier I get".

WORK SECTION

This section is made up of exercises designed to help you think about your anorexia in new ways, for example how it affects and is affected by your relationships with other people, particularly your family.

3

The exercises are divided into two groups: **Exploratory** Exercises and **On-going** Exercises. The On-going Exercises need to be completed over a period of time, and can give you an indication of how you are changing. The Exploratory Exercises can in fact be completed at any time, and perhaps more than once each, but we would recommend that you do tackle them early on.

Don't try to do the exercises all at once. You need to be able to think about what you have learnt from them and to talk about this with others. You may want to repeat an exercise, either to tackle it in a different way or to do it at a different time.

You can do the Exploratory Exercises with other people. Encourage your family to get involved, perhaps by doing some of the exercises for themselves and talking about them with you. Families where there is someone with anorexia often have problems with change in relationships, or some of the relationships between family members may be skewed. You can help the other people in your family by talking about these things, as well as helping yourself. (☛ Read "Families and How to Survive Them").

You can also do some of the exercises with friends. They are a good way of learning about other people, and about how they feel. People with anorexia often find personal relationships difficult and cut themselves off from others. These exercises are, in their different ways, about communicating with yourself and with other people.

We hope you find the exercises useful and interesting. You may want to make up some exercises of your own, or use the structured approach of the On-going Exercises in other areas of your life. We would certainly recommend that you continue to explore yourself and your life in whatever ways you feel able to.

Some of the exercises may upset you in some way. Be prepared for this. Try and find someone you can talk to about doing them, maybe a friend or your doctor perhaps. If you find a particular exercise too difficult then leave it for the time being and come back to it at another time.

3a

Effects of weight gain in anorexia nervosa

We have listed below some effects of gaining weight. We would like you to look at these effects and work out the "cost" and "benefit" of each - to you and perhaps others (separately). Not much is a simple cost or benefit, most items can be seen both as costs and benefits (the reason for you having anorexia is that this balance sheet meets your needs). Thus for instance "looking better" to others has advantages and disadvantages, but becomes an additional cost if everyone stops worrying about you when you know they should continue to do so.

	BENEFIT
e.g. You will look healthier	People will worry about me less
You may be more hungry	
You may be less hungry	
Your sleep may improve	I'll feel more relaxed
You may be less preoccupied with food	The strain on my mind may be lifted
There is less chance that you will binge	
You will look healthier	People will be pleased
You may become more angry	NONE
You may feel more anxious	NONE
You will become more sexually alert	
Other people will worry about you less	They can carry on peacefully with their own lives
You will lose your anorectic identity	I can look / learn how to be a new me

42

	COST
	People will worry about me less
	I'll lose my ... ...
	... ...
	B... ... for plump
	...n't ... to be more so
	... ...sider
	What's the point. I'd be no good in a rel'ship
	... ...

	BENEFIT
You will become more aware of what anorexia cost you	I can focus on that to spur me on
You will be better able to understand your anorexia	I can change my coping mechanisms
You will relate to other people better	I can feel I belong
You will feel fat	NONE
You will be on the road to recovery	Everyone will be happy
You will feel healthier	I'll feel more like getting involved, going out, working
You will be less constipated	
You will often feel full	I'll feel greedy
If you are female: Your breasts will develop	I'll be more mature looking
Your thighs will develop	NONE
Your periods will return	I'll have pain, embarassment worry, inconvenience

44

COST
I feel depressed about the grip it had on me and where I might be if things had gone better
I will realise my need for it
I'll begin dieting again and become irritable / depressed with others.
They did not
They don't need to
I'll feel as ... ... have children

Draw a Life Map

A life map is a way of representing the course of your life, including events and experiences that have been important or significant to you. One way of doing this is to see it as a road, with signposts marking the events and experiences. Or you may like to try imagining it as a journey over mountains, stormy seas, lakes, fields etc. You could then describe the different areas that you crossed at different times in your life. Try to include what are called "developmental milestones", that is things to do with growing up, like changing schools or starting your periods - together with things that you remember as being important like losing a friend, the birth of a brother or sister, or your parents having rows. The purpose of this exercise is that it can help you to see where you had got to before you developed anorexia. You might like to draw a second map, imagining where you might be now if you didn't have anorexia.

Make a Weight Biography

For this exercise you will probably need to join together several pieces of graph paper to make a larger sheet. Starting at the left hand side along the bottom of the page mark out the sheet in months and years up to your present age. On the upright axis mark out stones and pounds or kilograms starting from your birthweight up to your highest weight ever. Now mark on the graph any information you have about your weight at different periods of your life. You may need to ask other members of your family for some of this information. When you have plotted all the weights you know then join them together to make a graph of your weight since birth. Then go back to add information about important feelings and events that you included on your Life Map. This exercise may help you see that events in your life may have come to be linked very closely with your weight difficulties.

3a

Draw a Family Tree

Include anyone you regard as being part of your family. This will help you see the basic structure of your family and whether, for example, there are any patterns between the generations. Write in the names and ages of each person and describe them briefly. An example is given opposite.

Example of a family tree

Eric [79]
only child - worries a lot - needs looking after - eats too much of Eileen's cooking

Eileen (65)
very motherly - plump - spends all her time looking after Eric - very good cook.

divorced 1979

Brian [?]
drinking problem - not seen him for years - Mum gets letters from him sometimes - they make her cry

Sarah (60)
will do anything for anyone - interferes a lot - kind though - lonely, I think

Ellen (42)
divorced - 3 kids - always depressed - Dad worries about her

Ian [40]
lives in Australia - 2 kids - not seen him for years - Eric's favourite - a good laugh

married 1960

Bryan [38]
worries a lot and works too hard - on heart tablets - hard to talk to him - expects a lot

Jane (35)
emotional - loses her temper a lot - plump - always on a diet - always sorting other people out

Julie (32)
single - thin - graphic designer - career woman - beautiful

me (17)
?

David [16]
Mum's favourite - gets away with blue murder - loads of girlfriends - causes trouble

Ian [13]
Dad's favourite - brainy - good at everything - gets on my nerves

Who are you like?
Who do you want to be like?
Are there any patterns in the family?
What happens to the men?
What happens to the women?

49

Plot your Family Relationships

Draw a spot on a piece of paper. Imagine that this spot represents you. Then place the other people in your family around you according to how close you feel towards them now. So you should now have a central spot surrounded by several others. Repeat this exercise, remembering how things were the year before you became anorectic. The aim of this exercise is to help you see who you feel closest to and how great the distances are between you and other people in your family. It will also help you to see whether your relationships to the other members of your family have changed with your anorexia. If you find this exercise helpful you could also try to remember how things were when you were ten years old or at another time in your life that was in any way important. Look to see if there is any connection between the pattern with anorexia and other patterns.

Draw your Family Sitting in a Circle

Imagine who would sit next to whom (you can show them by letters or boxes - you don't need to be an artist). Now draw lines between different people according to the way people communicate with each other. You might like to do this according to who is closest to whom or by the methods people use to communicate, e.g. who shouts at whom, or who gives hugs etc. Use different colours for different ways of communicating. An example is given below. Again you can repeat this as for the previous exercise, noting any differences between varying times in your life. This exercise is intended to help you look at your family relationships in another way and consider the different ways in which people communicate or fail to communicate.

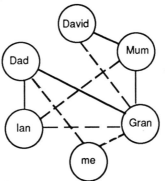

Who sits next to/opposite whom?
Who talks a lot to whom? → O————O
Who talks a little to whom? → O- - - -O
Who doesn't talk to whom? → O   O
How do you feel about the communication in the family?
Who would you like to sit by/opposite?
Who would you like to talk to you?
How would you like the communication to be different?

Imagine How other Members of your Family would describe You

Write down what each person would say about you. Does everyone say the same or are there differences? Check with the members of your family and find out what they think of your imaginary descriptions. You may also like to try this exercise by representing yourself visually by drawing a picture or making a collage of how other people see you. You can do this as you did the writing exercise. The purpose of this exercise is to find out whether your assessment of yourself is the same as the assessments others have of you. Often people have quite false ideas of other people's opinions of them.

Now that you have done this exercise, pause and reflect. Have you done it in relation to how you are now or how you were before your illness? Try to do it again imagining how it would all be now if you had not developed anorexia nervosa but had gone on pursuing your life at a normal adult weight.

On-going Exercises

Keeping a Diary

We strongly recommend that you keep a diary using, for instance, a small notebook. In this book we would recommend that you record the following information on a daily basis:

Information about your emotions that day - particularly those that arise in the context of the outlined STEPS. We would suggest that you avoid an emphasis on food or weight, because although these thoughts and feelings are important they are the thoughts and feelings that you are usually preoccupied with. The object of this exercise is to help you recognise new emotions and understand them in a new light. For instance you may be able to recognise emotions that on a certain day made it hard to eat.

3b

53

This diary may also help you to register progress that you make, by preventing you from forgetting insights that you develop and in looking back to see how you have changed.

The diary should certainly be a private thing, but at times it may be appropriate to use this written medium to show your thoughts to another selected person. Their perspective on your thoughts is bound to be at least slightly different from your own and hence useful.

If you can begin to gain weight then other changes can arise as we have already indicated, and you may like to record these in your diary in conjunction with the on-going weight chart (see, p.60). Try and make links between the two.

Keeping a Logbook

A logbook is a tool for self-assessment which we have found useful in treating people with anorexia in hospital. It differs from a diary in that it offers a structure for thinking about key issues to do with your problems.

To keep a logbook you will need a second notebook. The logbook itself has two sections:

▶ The first offers you a series of headings and we invite you to write down your current thoughts and feelings about each heading. We suggest you do this once a week at a set time, for example Sunday afternoon.

▶ The second section is a grid which can help you to assess which areas of your life are causing you difficulty. It then asks you to identify which resources you might use to help you tackle particular difficulties. We suggest you do this monthly and, as with the rest, at a set time. You will need to copy the headings and the grid into your notebook.

We have suggested that you do these things regularly, because our experience is that people's views, feelings and preoccupations change not only with time, but also with changes in weight. You will thus be able to look back over the time you have kept your logbook and see how things have changed, as well as which things have remained constant.

SECTION ONE

The Meaning of My Shape to Me
The Trigger(s) of My Illness and Their Meaning(s)
My Family Relationships; Then and Now
My Sense of Self; Social and Sexual
The Origins of My Anxiety
My Use of Avoidance to Deal with Conflict
My Family's Use of Avoidance to Deal with Conflict
My Other Moods
Why I Approach Others in the way that I do
My Present or Future Career; Why I have Chosen It
My Relationships with Authority
My Impulses and the way I manage them

SECTION TWO

☛ *On page 58 you will find a list of headings in table form.* Enter your present weight at the top of the table. Consider each heading as it applies to you now and rate how much of a problem it is to you at present, using this scale:

> 0 = Not a problem at present
> 1 = More of a problem than ever
> 2 = No real change
> 3 = Some change in the desired direction
> 4 = Much change in the desired direction

Enter your rating in the first column.

Now choose two, or at the most three, of the problems which are causing you most difficulty at the moment. Highlight these on the chart. From the list of resources pick those which you could use to help you tackle the problem, eg. if eating with others is the problem, perhaps you could talk about it with a friend and maybe practise with them, and/or use the dietary guidelines to make a meal which you could eat with others. Tick the resource(s) you have chosen in the space provided. You now have an outline plan which you can act on.

Every month repeat this exercise (you will need to make out some more tables yourself). Write what happened in respect of the two or three problems you tried to tackle. Then rate the list again, putting in your weight as before. You can then see whether problems are resolving or becoming more problematic. You may well decide to keep working on the same problems as before. Do not get discouraged if some problems get worse or return - this may actually be a positive sign. For example, cooking may not be a problem when you weigh 6 stones, but much more so when you are 8 stones. This is to be expected. You will probably also find that working on some problems is helpful to others indirectly.

A list of possible resources is given below. Add some of your own to this list if you have additional ones.

Resources:
G.P./Psychiatrist/Other professional help
Parents
Brothers and sisters
Friends
Partner
Self-help booklet
Structured exercises
Dietary guidelines
EDA/Other voluntary organisations
Reading
Painting/writing/creative activity
Social life/going out
Work
Counselling/therapy
Diary

3b

Example of grid to use in SECTION 2 of the Logbook

DATE: 6 / 2 / 90

RESOURCES

HEADINGS	Rating as a problem 0 - 4	GP/Psychiatrist Other Professional	EDA/Other Voluntary Organisations	Parents	Brothers/ Sisters	Friends	Partner
Asserting myself	2						
Being alone	2				✓	✓	
Being spontaneous	1						
Cooking	1						
Communicating	1						
Decision making	1						
Dietary education +menu planning	1						
Eating with others	1						
Expression of feelings	2						
Feeling in charge of myself	2						
Having fun	2						
Indulging myself	2						
Loving others	1						
My meanness	1						
My Self-esteem	2						
Normal exercise	2						
Owning my sexuality	2						
Serving normal portions	2						
Shopping for clothes/ cosmetics, etc.	0						
Shopping + spending money on food	2						
Socialising	2						
Thinking of others	2						
Touching others	0						
Trusting others	2						

58

RESOURCES

Self-help Booklet	Structured Exercises	Dietary Guidelines	Reading	Painting/ Writing Creative Activity	Social life/ Going out	Work	Counselling
			✓				
					✓		
✓			✓				

3b

59

Keeping a Weight Chart

We suggested that you weigh yourself once a week. It is easy to ignore the information this provides, and we would strongly recommend that you record your weight on a piece of graph paper - either in pounds, or stones and pounds, or kilograms against weeks. This chart will underline to you whether you are gaining weight, losing weight or keeping it the same. Remember what we said in Step 24 about a sensible rate of weight gain.

We also recommend that you draw a line across the chart showing your target weight, if you have decided to try and gain weight to this level, or the weight you are trying to aim at for the time being. If you are trying to stabilise your weight at any level (including target weight), allow a 2 lb (1 kg) band above your chosen weight to allow for normal weight fluctuation. Aim to keep your weight within this band.

Let us tell you that there are no mysteries to such a chart. Weight gain or loss always occurs for an easily understandable reason - which you will know if you are honest with yourself.

This chart will help you to notice particular difficulties in gaining weight to a fully normal level, i.e. above the 7 stone or less threshold referred to earlier. If you stop gaining weight before your "target weight" then you have taken control again (by eating less or vomiting/purging or whatever) - and you should ask "why?" What was so difficult about continuing to gain weight? We are not pushing you to continue gaining weight but it is important to understand why you have chosen a particular weight.

PRACTICAL INFORMATION SECTION

- Energy Balance
- Changing your behaviour
- Weight Tables
- Professional Help
- Useful Addresses
- Reading List

4

Energy Balance

Changing or stabilising your weight is not simply about what you eat. It is a consequence of a balance between the food you eat (and don't vomit) and how much energy you use - your "Energy Balance". This is complicated by what proportion of your body is water - your "Fluid Balance". To make it more complex, vomiting and using laxatives alter the balance of salts (electrolytes) in your body - your "Electrolyte Balance". Whilst not strictly about energy, these matters are closely related to energy, and are therefore included in this section.

FLUID BALANCE

Don't skip this section. Fluid balance is very important to understand. It is easy to ignore because it is not about calories, but it can drastically alter your weight. The balance is altered if you become dehydrated for any reason. Common reasons in anorexia include vomiting, using laxatives, restricting your fluid intake (markedly) or using caffeine or diuretics. Excessive fluid intake is discussed below, but it is very rare for your body to end up overhydrated (having too much water). This is because your kidneys cause you to produce more urine. If you are having too little fluid your kidneys produce as little urine as possible, but can only adjust to a certain point.

Weight loss through dehydration is confusing. Your

weight goes down, but if you drink a glass of water it may go up again. For this reason, as well as immediate physical well-being, it is important to avoid going without fluid as a means of weight control.

Bingeing and Vomiting

This is also dealt with in the "Energy Balance" and"Electrolyte Balance" sections. For this section it is important to recognise that in vomiting you are losing fluid. This is usually not a problem, but can be so if you do not take, and keep down, adequate fluid at other times. A further effect of bingeing can be a temporary increase in the amount of water in your body in response to having eaten a lot of carbohydrate. The effect is temporary, but can lead to panic about your weight going up.

Laxatives

It is important for you to know that laxatives do not rid your body of calories you have eaten by rushing food through your system in any way. They predominantly affect the large bowel which has the task of reabsorbing the large amount of water passing through it, back into the body. Laxatives irritate the large bowel and stop it from reabsorbing this water and hence users of laxatives continually pass large amounts of watery diarrhoea. Your weight will be affected by this loss of water - which must not be confused with loss of calories. Continual loss of water and essential substances like potassium (see "Electrolyte Balance") lost with it leads to serious physical problems.

4

Diuretics and Caffeine

Diuretics are drugs that have the effect of making you pass more urine. Not everyone recognises that caffeine (contained in coffee, tea and many drinks such as Coke) is also a relatively powerful diuretic. The loss of water achieved has the same effect as laxatives, you lose weight because you lose water, but only have to drink to regain this weight. Your weight can therefore change very quickly. Once again, this problem can make you physically ill and has an effect on your electrolytes (☛ see "Electrolyte Balance").

ELECTROLYTE BALANCE

In your body are a variety of salts, called electrolytes, one of the most important of which is potassium. Vomiting, laxatives and diuretics can all make you lose potassium. The effect of this can be very dangerous. Taking potassium replacements can be similarly dangerous. It is not always possible to gauge your need for potassium correctly, and too much potassium can be as dangerous as too little. This is another good reason to give up these particularly desperate ways of controlling your weight.

BALANCING YOUR DIET

As we state above, there is a balance between the food (and its energy content) you eat (and don't vomit) and how much energy you use. This should be a simple matter, but when you suffer from anorexia it can become very confused. It is therefore essential that you read this section carefully. A diet is not the same thing as a diet intended to lose weight, you can equally well have a diet that is aimed at gaining or stabilising your weight. Details of what we suggest you should eat are in the "Dietary Plans" section, but there are some general principles we discuss below.

For males with anorexia nervosa :
All the advice in this section and the "Dietary Plans" applies to you also. However, at any weight men have more muscle tissue than women do and as a result of this need more calories. Therefore you are likely to need the higher dietary plans to gain weight.

Vegetarianism
Ask yourself "When did I decide to become vegetarian?". If the answer is since you became anorectic, then it is likely the reasons for it lie with an avoidance of fat and calories and restriction of choice. It perhaps has given you a legitimate reason for saying "no" to eating the same food as your family. It is worth examining your reasons carefully and allow yourself to slowly reintroduce meat and fish.

If the answer is before you became anorectic then we have included sufficient alternatives to meat and fish in the meal plans. Vegetarianism and weight loss do not have to go hand in hand, but it can be harder to provide the calorie intakes we suggest. For example, a plate of vegetables looks a lot, but has a small calorie content for its size and therefore does not constitute a meal.

4

Exercise

Increased exercise in anorexia is common, and it occurs for a number of reasons. One of these reasons is an attempt to "burn off" calories. Therefore, whether you are aiming to stabilise your weight or gain weight you may very well be tempted to increase the amount of exercise you are doing when you make changes to your diet. The dietary plans will only be of value to you if you do not increase your exercise. The more active you are the more calories you will need.

Bingeing and Vomiting

If you vomit after a meal or binge and vomit at any time you must eat your next planned meal or snack. Otherwise, by skipping the next meal you will be even more hungry and therefore more likely to binge or overeat soon after, continuing a very vicious circle.

Fluid intake

You may have become accustomed to drinking large quantities of fluid throughout the day to fill you up and avoid feeling hungry. An adequate amount of fluid is between 1.5 - 2 litres (8 - 10 cups) drunk throughout the day. Avoid drinking just before you eat.

DIETARY PLANS

We have attached three dietary plans:

A   contains between 1000 - 1100 kcal
B   contains between 1500 - 1600 kcal
C   contains between 2000 - 2100 kcal.

The plans are as precise as is practicable when providing a varied diet. However, the variety of foods is deliberately limited as we know you will find it difficult to make choices about what you eat. You may find it easiest to literally rotate the choices given on a daily basis.

We suggest you eat three meals every day with small mid-meal snacks where stated. You may be worried about eating breakfast having got used to eating only at the end of the day. Each of the dietary plans ensures you can eat both at the beginning and the end of the day. Define your mealtimes to ensure you know when you are going to eat and do not make excuses about insufficient time to do so.

Each plan contains a snack meal at lunch and a cooked meal in the evening; these can be exchanged if it fits in better with your lifestyle. Each meal, whatever the calorie content, contains starch, protein and vegetables together with fruit and/or dessert. Many anorectics will eat large quantities of vegetables and/or salad. A plate piled high with vegetables leaves little room for other foods, therefore make an effort to put vegetables on your plate after you have served the portions of other foods.

4

Alternatively, limit yourself to 3 tablespoons of cooked vegetables OR a side plate/individual salad bowl of salad.

You may find buying ready-prepared single portion meals easier than cooking for yourself. There is now a wide variety available most of which have the calorie content stated on the pack. For this reason we have recommended which meals to buy, by the calorie content, to fit in with each of the plans.

You may find it useful to see the dietary plans as prescriptions as, whatever stage you are at in the process of recovery, food is a necessary part of your overall well-being.

Which plan ?

The dietary plans have been carefully thought out to allow you to progressively increase your calorie intake by slowly increasing the number of portions of the same foods you eat. In addition a limited number of different foods are slowly incorporated.

If your weight is well below 7 stones then your calorie requirements will be very small. We would suggest you take plan A and slowly increase your present diet to that level initially. Please note that a diet containing only 1000 kcal or less is not nutritionally complete enough with respect to the micronutrients i.e. vitamins and minerals, for long term use. There is a risk this would lead to deficiencies. There is very little known of the requirements of someone living at a lower than normal body weight for long periods of time, in some instances many years. If you do continue to eat such a low calorie diet you will need more specific dietary advice with respect to vitamin and mineral supplementation.

If you are going to try to stabilise your weight in the region of 6 - 7 stones then depending on your age and height you will need to eat between 1000 - 1600 kcal per day, outlined as plans A and B. Therefore we suggest you start with meal plan A and slowly increase the portions as outlined until you are eating the diet that maintains your weight. Make only one increase at a time so that you are gaining weight in a controlled way. You will see from your weekly weight chart what effect the increase has on your weight. If your weight remains the same for two weighings then this is the time to increase your intake again so that you are gaining weight in a controlled, stepwise manner. Be honest with yourself and ensure you are eating everything as stated on your plan at each stage: no more and no less.

If you are going to gain weight past 7 stones then start with meal plan B and, in the same way as above, slowly increase your intake to that of plan C. Remember, make only one increase at a time to see what effect it has on your weight. Taller women and men are more likely to need a higher calorie intake than 2000 - 2100 kcal (plan C) to continue gaining weight.

To increase your intake above plan C add the following foods into your eating plan one at a time in the same way as previously suggested according to your weight gain. These foods will gradually increase your calorie intake to between 3000 - 3100 kcal.

4

1. 1 cup of milk (silver top) 200ml at bedtime.
2. 2 digestive biscuits mid-morning.
3. Any 2 digestive biscuits to be replaced with 1 bar of chocolate

    e.g.   4-finger Kit-Kat
          or a Twix bar
          or a 50g bar of chocolate

4. 1 boiled egg plus 150ml fruit juice at breakfast.
5. 1 slice of bread plus 1 teaspoon of butter/ margarine at lunch.
6. Pudding and custard to replace individual dessert

    e.g. small fruit pie plus 150ml of custard; or 2 tablespoons of fruit crumble plus 150ml of custard.

7. 1 cup of milk at mid-morning.

Plan your meals the day before or weekly so that you know what you are going to eat. Use the eating plans to do this and stick with your plan! Do not leave your decisions until mealtimes as you are likely to find it very difficult to then make a choice.

You know you can run rings round these guidelines if you choose to. If you want to change you will need to be honest here. Coping with these changes in your diet and their effect on your weight and shape will enable you more effectively to confront and to begin to deal with all the other issues bearing on your anorexia nervosa, even if your present intention is not to shed it completely.

How to eat at a normal weight

Once you have reached your target weight the next step will be to learn how much food you need to maintain it. We know how worried you will be about continuing to gain weight above target weight, and going out of control. It is for this reason we have recommended you gain weight in the stepwise manner so that you know how much to eat to maintain it before making the next step up each time. As you approach target weight in this way it will not be necessary to decrease your diet to stop gaining weight but rather to stop increasing it.

It is all about getting the balance right between how much to eat and how much activity. You will need to learn to maintain your weight within your "target band" and this will mean tolerating small weight changes, i.e. your weight fluctuating up and down along a straight line without you making sudden and drastic changes to your diet. It is important that you continue not to vomit and purge and that you limit your exercise. We recommend you do not involve yourself in any regular, formal exercise or sport until you have had a considerable period of time learning to maintain your weight without it, say six months.

The main reason why anorectics exercise is to burn up calories and there will be a strong temptation for you to decrease your diet if you feel you are inactive or have a compulsive feeling of having to exercise to justify eating, particularly as you try to hold your weight steady. It is important for you to know that nearly threequarters (75%) of everybody's calorie intake is needed just to keep them alive, not running around.

4

71

It is going to take a long time before you will be able to rely on feelings of hunger and satiety to guide you. You may not even experience or recognise feelings of hunger at a normal weight for some time. There are going to be many mealtimes when you do not "feel like eating"; the reasons for this are more likely to be related to feelings of worry or anxiety, panic about eating too much or going out of control. It is because these feelings get confused and you become focussed on how much or how little to eat at these meals that we strongly recommend you eat according to your eating plan in a prescribed manner for as long as it takes.

Only then does it become safer to begin to take risks and learn to eat in an unplanned way, for instance at a friend's house or in a restuarant, for an occasional meal if you have the familiar structure surrounding you.

Allow yourself very slowly to introduce other foods into your plan, especially foods you like!

EATING PLANS

	A No. of portions	B No. of portions	C No. of portions
BREAKFAST			
Cereal	1	1	1
bread	1	2	2
fat	1	2	2
jam/marmalade	-	-	2 teaspoons
MID-MORNING			
fruit	-	1	1
LUNCH			
bread	1	2	2
protein	1	1	2
fat	1	2	2
salad/vegetables	✓	✓	✓
fruit	1	1	1
chocolate biscuit	-	-	1
MID-AFTERNOON			
fruit	1	-	1
digestive biscuits	-	1	2
EVENING MEAL			
Starch	1½	1 ½	2
protein	1	2	2
fat	1	1	2
salad/vegetables	✓	✓	✓
fruit	1	-	-
dessert	-	1	1
BEDTIME			
Digestive biscuit	-	1	2
MILK throughout the day	1	1	1

☛ *(See overleaf for details of what constitutes a 'portion')*

4

73

Conversion factor: 1 oz = 25g

1 cup = 1 standard breakfast cup, 200mls

STARCH

1 PORTION is:

Bread: 1 slice from a large medium-sliced loaf:
wholemeal or white

Potato: jacket or boiled (100g)
mashed: 1 rounded tablespoon

Rice: boiled: 2 rounded tablespoons
(weight before cooking 25g)

Pasta: boiled: 2 rounded tablespoons
(weight before cooking 25g)

Breakfast Cereals: Branflakes OR cornflakes:1 cup (25g)
Weetabix: 2
Muesli: $1/2$ cup (25g)

PROTEIN

1 PORTION is:

For lunch:

Eggs: 1 size 2
Cheese: Cheddar type 25g
Cottage cheese: 1 small tub
Baked beans: $1/2$ of a 225g tin OR
2 tablespoons
Tuna fish: $1/2$ of a 100g tin

For evening meal:

Red meat: 50g cooked weight
Chicken: 50g cooked weight
White fish: 100g cooked weight
Beans eg. kidney, haricot
50g before soaking
100g after soaking or tinned
Lentils: 25g (dry weight)

FAT

1 PORTION is:

Butter/margarine:	1 teaspoon
Vegetable oils:	1 teaspoon
Low fat spreads:	2 teaspoons

MILK

1 PORTION is:

Silver top:	$\frac{1}{2}$ pint
Semi-skimmed:	$\frac{2}{3}$ pint

FRUIT

1 PORTION is:

Apple OR orange OR pear:	1 medium
Banana:	1 small

DESSERT

1 PORTION is:

1 individual pot of dessert such as: | fruit yoghurt
         NOT 'DIET' VARIETIES ← | rice pudding
                              | trifle

A dessert such as the above should contain between 135 - 150 kcal

Vanilla ice cream: 75g

CHOCOLATE BISCUIT

1 PORTION is:

Jacobs Club biscuit:	1
Penguin biscuit:	1
2 finger Kit-Kat:	1

Ready prepared meals for the evening meal:

	A	B	C
Calorie content:	250-300 kcal	350-400 kcal	450-500 kcal

4

Changing your behaviour
- Bingeing, vomiting laxative abuse,
  over-exercising.

These suggestions may help you if you want to stop, say abusing laxatives, but find that you can't just give it up then and there.

There are two 'golden rules' about changing your behaviour this way:

- **Go slowly**
- **Try to change a little at a time**

We say this because there will be powerful reasons why you are behaving as you are and it will take time to adjust to not behaving this way.

WHAT ARE YOU DOING?

This question might seem obvious, but you need to be clear about your behaviour before you can change it. For example, if you are bingeing, how often are you doing it, how long does a binge last, what happens afterwards, what sets it off? We suggest you keep a diary for at least one week, in which you note down the behaviour under these headings (or choose others if you feel they are more suitable):

What time did it start?
What was I doing before/when it started?

How did I feel before/when it started?
What did I do then?
How long did I do it for?
How did I feel while doing it?
What made me stop?
What happened after I had stopped?
How did I feel afterwards?

ESTABLISHING PATTERNS

When you have done that you should have to hand a very clear and detailed description of the behaviour which you would like to change. Remember that it's important to fill the diary in throughout the week and not guess or put down what you think is happening from memory.

Look at what you have written. Are there any patterns to your behaviour? Do you do things at the same time of the day or in similar situations? Do you always feel the same? What stops you doing it? Do you always do things the same way when the behaviour occurs? Does it relate at all to your current efforts in relation to STEPS 1 - 9? Just identifying some of these things may be *helpful in breaking the pattern (☛ see below).*

If there are no established patterns, or very few, then your first step is probably to try and regularize your behaviour. This will make it easier to tackle change. Here are some suggestions:

4

- Try to keep to regular times - either periods of the day (e.g. morning/evening) or specific times (e.g. 6-9 p.m.). Aim for a regular pattern such as every day or every other day or once a week, even if that means slightly increasing the number of times the behaviour occurs. You are aiming for some measure of control - that is, you decide when the behaviour will occur. Try not to do it outside the times you have set.

- Try to do the same thing every time the behaviour occurs - for instance eat the same amount of food, do the same amount of exercise, take the same number of laxatives. Try not to do it in a more ritualistic way than you have been doing - again, the aim is that you decide what you are going to do. It also means you may have to plan it.

- Try to make sure the behaviour occurs in the same place every time, so that you always binge in the same place, take the same route for jogging, take the laxatives in the same place.

When you are 'free' of the behaviour, in between times, then try to make sure that you look after yourself, especially in those areas which might be suffering as a result of what you are doing - like getting some rest if you are over-exercising, drinking enough fluids if you are dehydrating yourself, eating your 'usual' diet in between binges or after vomiting. You may find this hard to do, but we recommend that you try.

78

CHANGING THE PATTERN

First make a list of things which you could see as rewards for yourself. Try not to choose any which are related to food, eating or exercise. They may be social contact with others, hobbies or activities, shopping, going to the cinema etc., as well as small things, like using a certain perfume, having a bath, doing your hair, or writing letters. You will need small rewards as well as bigger ones. You will be using these to reward yourself for the changes you are able to make. If you have trouble doing this, then ask someone to help you. As with most of the work in this booklet, it's easier to tackle these things if you have help and support from others, especially your family, and it's especially relevant when trying to change your behaviour.

You should by now have a pattern of behaviour which you want to change. You are going to try to change it in stages. First you need to identify which part you are going to change and how you are going to change it. You will have to decide this for yourself, using the information you've gathered so far, for example:

▶ You are bingeing and vomiting three times a day. You decide to try to cut it down to twice a day. You know that you can sometimes manage to get through the morning without bingeing. You decide to try not to binge before noon, but to keep to the bingeing on the other two occasions each day.

▶ You always vomit straight after every meal. You decide to try and wait 10 minutes after each meal before going to the toilet to vomit.

4

or:

▶ You are taking 50 laxatives a day. You decide to take 40 a day.

Write down what your behaviour is at present. Then write down what you want it to be, as in the examples above. Try to change only one thing at a time. Use your diary and your identified pattern to help you find alternatives for the behaviour if necessary. For example, if other people being around stops you vomiting, make sure you are with others when you are trying not to vomit, at least initially. Be aware of what things help you make changes, so that you can use them in future.

Every time you succeed, allow yourself a small reward. Use a chart if you find that helpful. When you have managed to achieve the change for a whole week, allow yourself a bigger reward. You can then decide to make a further change, if that seems appropriate. Do this in the same way as before.

You may think that this method is too slow, or the changes insignificant. However, it is not just the actual change that is important, but also the process of being able to change. You may well have felt that nothing could be done, or that you could never control these aspects of your behaviour in a healthy way. So just being able to make any change could be important in itself. For this reason you may find that changes get easier after a while, or that you can make bigger changes at a time. Guard against pushing yourself too hard, though.

IF YOU CAN'T CHANGE OR YOU GET STUCK

Don't expect to be able to change something immediately, or without any hitches. You have to practise! Allow yourself three or four weeks of trying. If you still can't do it, then was it for one of the following reasons:

▶ Did you try to change too much at once?
If so, try to make a smaller change.

▶ Did you try to change the most difficult thing?
If so, try to make an easier change. You don't have to take the hardest option.

▶ Did you choose the right time to make changes?
If not, consider whether you are ready for change at the moment, or whether you are too preoccupied with other things.

▶ Did you have enough help?
Maybe you tried without help, or need help with other aspects of your life, (e.g. STEPS 1-9), so didn't have enough resources to make the change.

▶ Do you need a rest from changes?
If you find you get stuck after making some changes, then consider the possibility that you may need a break from changing. Try instead to maintain the change you have made for a while.

4

▶ Do you really want to change?
  This may seem like a tough question, but
  repeated failure brings up the possibility
  that the part of you that does not want to
  change at present is too powerful. You
  may need help to work out why that is so.

These are only guidelines to help you and they can't
possibly be comprehensive. You will need to work out
your own timetable for change and we hope that some
of these suggestions will prove useful. Again
remember that you don't have to change everything at
once and that change is usually difficult. Gradual,
stepwise change may prove to be the best option in
the long run. Try to be patient and allow yourself
plenty of time.

Weight Tables

The tables below are intended to help you realise the weight at which you should aim. As we mention elsewhere, we recommend that you look at the weight for someone of your sex, your height, and your age at the onset of your major "dieting". This will be a "normal weight" based on figures for a normal population in the UK gathered in the 1940s. Contrary to what you may think, these weights are lighter than more recent surveys. We recommend these weights because they are more in keeping with what people want (as opposed to what they are), they may be healthier, and because experience shows that they have been successful in helping people to overcome anorexia. We are not recommending your target weight as the weight at which you will feel best, look best, live longest or whatever. It is a weight at which you stand the best chance of avoiding the emotional and physical costs of anorexia. We feel sure that you will argue with these figures, but we warn you that your objections are likely to spring defensively from your anorexia.

We do not give weights for people with an onset before the age of 15, or after the age of 27. Before the age of 15 the body is growing at very variable rates for different individuals, and hence general advice is hard to give. An onset of anorexia after 27 does occur but is rare. If you are unsure it is probably advisable to discuss a target weight with your local doctor, or look in *Anorexia Nervosa: Let Me Be* for further details.

4

FEMALES:

Height (ins)		15	16	17	18	19	20	21	22	23	24	27
							lbs					
56		84	90	94	96	97	98	98	98	98	99	100
57		88	93	97	99	100	101	101	102	102	102	103
58		92	97	101	102	103	104	104	105	105	106	106
59		96	100	104	105	106	107	108	108	108	109	109
60		100	104	107	109	110	110	111	111	111	112	112
61		104	107	110	112	113	114	114	114	114	115	116
62		108	111	113	115	116	117	117	118	118	118	119
63		112	114	117	118	119	120	120	121	121	121	122
64		115	118	120	121	122	123	124	124	124	124	125
65		119	121	123	125	126	126	127	127	127	127	128
66		123	125	126	128	129	130	130	130	130	130	131
67		127	128	129	131	132	133	133	133	134	134	134
68		131	132	133	134	135	136	136	137	137	136	137
69		135	135	136	137	138	139	140	140	140	140	140
70		139	139	139	141	142	142	143	143	143	143	144

MALES:

Height (ins)	Age 15	16	17	18	19	20	21	22	23	24	27
	lbs										
60	96	99	103	106	109	111	114	115	116	117	118
61	101	104	107	110	112	115	117	119	120	121	121
62	105	108	111	113	116	119	121	122	124	124	125
63	109	112	115	117	120	122	124	126	127	128	129
64	113	116	119	121	124	126	128	130	131	132	132
65	117	120	123	125	128	130	132	133	134	135	136
66	122	124	127	129	132	134	135	137	138	139	140
67	126	128	131	133	135	137	139	140	142	142	144
68	130	132	135	137	139	141	142	144	145	146	147
69	134	136	139	141	143	145	146	148	149	150	151
70	138	140	143	145	147	148	150	151	152	153	155
71	143	145	147	148	150	152	153	155	156	157	158
72	147	149	151	152	154	156	157	158	160	160	162
73	151	153	155	156	158	159	160	162	163	164	166
74	155	157	159	160	162	163	164	166	167	168	169

4

UNITS OF WEIGHT CONVERSION TABLES

lb	stone	lb	kg	lb	stone	lb	kg
56	4	0	25.4	86	6	2	39.0
57	4	1	25.9	87	6	3	39.5
58	4	2	26.3	88	6	4	39.9
59	4	3	26.8	89	6	5	40.4
60	4	4	27.2	90	6	6	40.8
61	4	5	27.7	91	6	7	41.3
62	4	6	28.1	92	6	8	41.7
63	4	7	28.6	93	6	9	42.2
64	4	8	29.0	94	6	10	42.6
65	4	9	29.5	95	6	11	43.1
66	4	10	29.9	96	6	12	43.6
67	4	11	30.4	97	6	13	44.0
68	4	12	30.8	98	7	0	44.5
69	4	13	31.3	99	7	1	44.9
70	5	0	31.8	100	7	2	45.4
71	5	1	32.2	101	7	3	45.8
72	5	2	32.7	102	7	4	46.3
73	5	3	33.1	103	7	5	46.7
74	5	4	33.6	104	7	6	47.2
75	5	5	34.0	105	7	7	47.6
76	5	6	34.5	106	7	8	48.1
77	5	7	34.9	107	7	9	48.5
78	5	8	35.4	108	7	10	49.0
79	5	9	35.8	109	7	11	49.4
80	5	10	36.3	110	7	12	49.9
81	5	11	36.7	111	7	13	50.4
82	5	12	37.2	112	8	0	50.8
83	5	13	37.7	113	8	1	51.3
84	6	0	38.1	114	8	2	51.7
85	6	1	38.6	115	8	3	52.2

UNITS OF WEIGHT CONVERSION TABLES

lb	stone	lb	kg	lb	stone	lb	kg
116	8	4	52.6	146	10	6	66.2
117	8	5	53.1	147	10	7	66.7
118	8	6	53.5	148	10	8	67.1
119	8	7	54.0	149	10	9	67.6
120	8	8	54.4	150	10	10	68.0
121	8	9	54.9	151	10	11	68.5
122	8	10	55.3	152	10	12	69.0
123	8	11	55.8	153	10	13	69.4
124	8	12	56.3	154	11	0	69.9
125	8	13	56.7	155	11	1	70.3
126	9	0	57.2	156	11	2	70.8
127	9	1	57.6	157	11	3	71.2
128	9	2	58.1	158	11	4	71.7
129	9	3	58.5	159	11	5	72.1
130	9	4	59.0	160	11	6	72.6
131	9	5	59.4	161	11	7	73.0
132	9	6	59.9	162	11	8	73.5
133	9	7	60.3	163	11	9	73.9
134	9	8	60.8	164	11	10	74.4
135	9	9	61.2	165	11	11	74.8
136	9	10	61.7	166	11	12	75.3
137	9	11	62.1	167	11	13	75.8
138	9	12	62.6	168	12	0	76.2
139	9	13	63.1	169	12	1	76.7
140	10	0	63.5	170	12	2	77.1
141	10	1	64.0	171	12	3	77.6
142	10	2	64.4	172	12	4	78.0
143	10	3	64.9	173	12	5	78.5
144	10	4	65.3	174	12	6	78.9
145	10	5	65.8	175	12	7	79.4

4

Professional Help

The good news is that there are many sources of professional help open to you in the U.K. The bad news is that the type of help available varies tremendously and it is not always easy to hit on what is right for you. Some help is available on the NHS and some you will be asked to pay for. This section is intended to give you a little more guidance about what is available and what to expect from the various areas of help. If it is difficult to know what sort of help to choose then ask someone to go over the options with you and discuss them. Remember that any help which is going to be useful is not going to make you feel wholly comfortable - sometimes it may be very challenging - but ideally it should offer you some sort of support as well as working towards change. Remember too, that there are no "magic" solutions which are suddenly going to make things better. As we have stressed elsewhere in this booklet, you need to give yourself time to change and it will take time. Be prepared for that.

NHS SERVICES

Primary Health Care Services-available through G.P.
Your General Practitioner is usually your first port of call for access to NHS services. He or she can either try to help you directly or refer you to a hospital doctor or therapist. Other people who may be attached to your G.P.'s practice are a dietician, a

counsellor, and a community psychiatric nurse. Ask your G.P. what is available in your practice, depending on what sort of help you need. If there is nothing suitable then ask to be referred to a consultant who has some experience with psychiatric or psychological problems or who is professionally interested in eating disorders. You can also ask to be referred to a psychologist if that seems more appropriate, or to a psychotherapy department if there is one in your area. Your family may also be able to receive help from these sources.

NHS Hospital Services

At present, most hospitals in the country have responsibility for defined geographical areas (catchment areas) which they serve. This can limit your choice in the first instance. You may be referred to a medical consultant or to a psychiatrist and this will affect the type of treatment approach, which will also depend to some extent on the severity of your anorexia. Some hospital services will pay more attention to physical problems and your eating, whereas some will also help you with your emotional and psychological needs. On balance, you are more likely to get help for both from a psychiatric service.

Emergencies

It is not uncommon for people suffering from anorexia to be admitted to hospital as a result of a crisis, and they may then find themselves either on a medical ward for rehydration or emergency refeeding or perhaps in a psychiatric hospital on a Section of the

4

Mental Health Act (which means they can be kept in hospital for their own good even if they don't want to be there). There is no doubt that these can be very unpleasant experiences, but those around the sufferer may well feel that there is no alternative at the time. Sufferers themselves are most likely to seek urgent medical help if bingeing is getting out of control. Under these circumstances you may not be seeking help to shed your anorexia nervosa but to sustain it! We are in no doubt that it is preferable to ask for help for your anorexia before things get out of hand like this.

Out-patient treatment.

When you are referred to a hospital, and it is not an emergency, you will be seen first in outpatients, or occasionally at home. The purpose of this first meeting is to try and work out what the problems are and how best to help you. If you want help and your physical state is not putting you at risk, then you may well be offered out-patient treatment, either individually or with your family. It is our experience that most anorectics would prefer this option, and it's certainly less drastic than coming into hospital. However, such a preference may be dictated by good or bad (evasive) reasons. It certainly means you have to take a lot more responsibility for helping yourself and working on things at home. For some people it's the best option at this stage but for others it's not enough. Out-patient treatment may be provided by various people such as doctors, psychologists, social workers, nurses and dieticians. In some cases you may be allocated a community psychiatric nurse who will come and see you and your family at home.

Day-patient treatment

Some psychiatric hospitals have day-patient units where you can get intensive support without having to come into hospital. Usually they involve you going every day of the week for a time. Often they work in groups and may also include individual and family work. Occupational therapy is also used a good deal. They are a useful bridge between out-patient and in-patient care.

In-patient treatment

For some people admission to hospital will be advised or become necessary. In most cases this will happen because out-patient treatment is not working or because it would not or does not provide enough support for the sufferer. (Some people need more support than others.) Many anorectics are very afraid of this option because they see it as threatening their control over their anorexia. However you should expect that most doctors and nurses genuinely want to help people with problems and it is worth giving them a chance. You'll need to bear in mind that they are not perfect and also that anorexia is not one of the most common problems that they have to deal with, so they may not have a lot of experience in dealing with your particular anxieties and difficulties. However, there is no reason why they shouldn't learn from helping you!

Specialist eating disorder units

There are about a dozen hospitals in the country which have units specializing in the treatment of eating disorders. They have grown up fairly randomly

4

91

and tend to be attached to large teaching hospitals. Predictably, the South of England is best served by such units. Some of them operate strict catchment area criteria while others will see people from other areas but are limited in their resources and by the demand on their services. Most of them have quite long waiting lists for appointments, which means they can't usually help in emergencies. Treatments available are usually out-patient and in-patient, with only one hospital offering a specialized day-patient service, and approaches to anorexia do vary between the units. If you would like to be referred to such a unit, then ask your G.P. or the hospital doctor you are currently seeing.

PRIVATE TREATMENT

Private hospital services

There are a number of doctors and hospitals which will treat anorectics privately. Some of them have specialist eating disorder programmes. They are usually very expensive and may not be an option unless you have private health insurance. You can ask your G.P. for details of private hospital services and doctors, or ask in your local library for a directory of such services.

Private counselling and psychotherapy

Counselling and psychotherapy are, in our view, important aids to recovery from anorexia (☞ *see STEP 30)*. There are many private therapists and counsellors across the country and it can be difficult to know how to choose someone suitable and reliable. Such help is not always cheap, but usually much less expensive than private medicine, and many counsellors and therapists charge sliding scale fees according to your income. Again it may be worth asking your G.P. or someone in your occupational health department if they can recommend someone - most trained therapists are not allowed to advertise their services. Perhaps someone in your school or your church may also know of a good counsellor, or the local Citizen's Advice Bureau may have a list. The Eating Disorders Association holds a list of counsellors and psychotherapists who are willing to help people with anorexia. ☛ *Other such resources are listed on pages 95-96.* When you have found someone, be critical. For you especially, it is important that you work with someone who will take your weight and eating seriously, and not all counsellors and therapists feel happy about getting involved with those issues. Equally it is important that you like and feel supported by the therapist, at least in part. If you feel you really can't get on with someone, then look again. It's vital that you find someone you can learn to trust and depend on.

Family and marital/couple therapy can also be obtained privately. ☛ *See the resource list on pp.95-96 for contacts.*

Other private treatments

There are a variety of other treatments which people try, like acupuncture, hypnotherapy, relaxation, massage, allergy treatments, homeopathy, etc. The

4

93

same advice applies as for private psychotherapy. Some of these treatments, for instance those which help with relaxation, can provide useful additional support to someone who is trying to come to terms with life either at normal weight or as an anorectic. Some of them are, frankly, useless to an anorectic and may cost a fortune. Beware of any treatment which claims certain success or quick results. We and you know that things are much more complex than that. So, as you can see, getting the help you need and want may not always be straightforward. As we said before, don't give up if you can't find the right help immediately. This booklet itself reflects one of our own efforts to help you and others like you who wish that things could be better in these respects.

Useful Addresses

EATING DISORDERS ASSOCIATION
at:

Sackville Place,   and   The Priory Centre
44 Magdalen Street   11 Priory Road
Norwich,   High Wycombe
Norfolk NR3 1JE   Bucks HP13 6SL
Tel: 0603-621414   Tel: 0494-21431

The Eating Disorders Association is a nationwide organisation which aims to offer help and advice to sufferers and their families. They offer a telephone helpline, answer letters and have a huge list of resources available to people suffering from eating disorders. They also run a network of self-help groups for sufferers and sometimes their families. They publish a regular newsletter for members.

BRITISH ASSOCIATION FOR COUNSELLING

37a Sheep Street
Rugby
Warwickshire CV21 3BX

The BAC can give you advice on finding a reputable counsellor or therapist in your area. They also publish an annual directory of such services, which you should be able to get from your local library.

RELATE (formerly the Marriage Guidance Council)

Herbert Gray College
Little Church Street
Rugby
Warwickshire CV21 3AP.

Relate offers counselling to people who are having relationship difficulties (not only those who are married). Their counsellors are well trained and there is a branch in most areas. Look in your local telephone directory or contact the above address for more information.

THE WOMEN'S THERAPY CENTRE

9 Manor Gardens
London N7

The Women's Therapy Centre offers low-cost therapy for women as well as day and weekend workshops, some of which focus on eating problems. They work from a feminist standpoint which might not suit everyone. You can get an idea of their approach from reading Marilyn Lawrence's book (☛ see Reading List). Write to them for details of therapy and workshops.

Reading List

BOOKS ON ANOREXIA NERVOSA

Anorexia Nervosa : Let Me Be.
by A.H.Crisp
published by Academic Press

Our general approach is reflected in detail in this book. It attempts to link the social, cultural, personal and physical aspects of the condition both in terms of its development and its treatment. Against this background, towards the end of the book, ten patients, and sometimes their families, describe their own experiences of the condition. You may want to read these first. Then have a go at reading the book through. The author suggests that "Anorexia nervosa is a biological solution to an existential problem". What do you think?

The Golden Cage
by Hilda Bruch
published by Open Books

This book is a classic of its kind. We differ in our views only in degree from Dr. Bruch who presents anorexia nervosa as the "pursuit of thinness" as though this was a choice of identity rather than a flight to a refuge permitting no alternative. She also emphasises the primacy of food rather than body shape in her attempt to understand the factors that precede anorexia nervosa during childhood and to relate them to the illness. We suggest you read this alongside *"Let Me Be"*, searching out the differences and similarities of approach.

4

Anorexia Nervosa
by R.L.Palmer
published by Penguin Books

This is a very useful and comprehensive book which aims to help you make some sense of anorexia nervosa and also of any hospital treatment you have received or may be thinking of trying. It is written by a doctor and concentrates largely on medical approaches to anorexia, but it doesn't do this in a narrow-minded way. It is easy to read and should help you and your family be better informed about anorexia.

The Anorexic Experience
by Marilyn Lawrence
published by The Women's Press

This book is written by a therapist at the Women's Therapy Centre in London. She has had a great deal of experience in working with women suffering from anorexia and her views are based on a feminist approach to the problems young women face in life. Her approach is in no way extreme and the book offers a useful, non-medical way of looking at anorexia. It is readable, informative and encouraging and includes plenty of examples of women's differing experiences of having anorexia. The book invites you to choose whether or not to tackle your difficulties and how to find a way of doing this that suits you, in a very supportive way.

The Art of Starvation
by Sheila MacLeod
published by Virago

This book should be seen as consisting of two parts. The first part involves Sheila MacLeod's very personal

98

description of her childhood and the experiences she sees, with hindsight, as being important influences on her subsequent anorexia. Her account of family life and her school days is particularly evocative and well written. The second part, or aspect, of this book revolves around the author's own view of how and why people develop (choose) anorexia as a means of coping and self determination. In this she discusses theoretical issues, as well as her own attempts at recovery. This is quite technical at times, and generally harder going for the reader.

Overall, a worthwhile book, which would probably benefit from being read around, and shortly after, the time of reaching target weight.

Eating your Heart out
by Julia Buckroyd
published by Optima Books

This book is about eating difficulties in general, not just anorexia, and it is aimed at helping you think about what underlies your eating disorder. It is easy to read and develops some of the ideas contained here. It should set you thinking!

Video: The Treatment - Anorexia Nervosa.

This half-hour long presentation derives from a Thames Television programme first broadcast in 1987. It was subsequently donated to the Catherine Dunbar (Anorexia) Trust. It presents our own view of the disorder, our attempt to assess its nature and to help. It can be purchased at cost price from us on enquiry at our address (☛ *p.2*). It is available for personal and group educational purposes and cannot be shown to audiences for profit.

4

BOOKS ABOUT FAMILIES AND RELATIONSHIPS

Families and How to Survive Them
by Robin Skynner and John Cleese
published by Methuen

This is a very popular and charming book which explains simply and clearly the process of development of the personality and how this is affected by the family's established patterns of communication.
It describes in an amusing and entertaining way basic psychological concepts. We highly recommend this book which has particular relevance to your attempts to understand your personality, your family relationships and the ways in which you relate to others.

Games People Play
by E. Berne
published by Deutsch. (Also available in paperback, published by Penguin Books)

This book is about the different ways in which people relate to each other. The author looks at them as "games" in which the participants "agree" to take on different roles according to what they hope to gain from their relationships. People tend to play similar roles even in different relationships. This book can help you look at the way you relate to others and how they in their turn relate, both to you and to other people. You may be able to find patterns of relating. The book is fairly scholarly, but is also intended for a wider audience.

BOOKS ABOUT SEXUALITY AND RELATIONSHIPS

First love, first sex: a practical guide to relationships.
by Kaye Wellings
published by Thorsons Publishing Group.

This book is recommended by the Family Planning Association, and is a clear, comprehensive and readable guide to all aspects of intimate and sexual relationships. Although its title suggests it is a "beginners book", it nevertheless contains a lot of information of use to anyone who has anxieties about or difficulties with intimate relationships. It is full of illustrations and well worth buying for yourself.

Girls and sex;
Boys and sex
by Wardell B. Pomeroy
published by Penguin.

These books are written from years of experience counselling young people on sexuality. They are direct and informative and aim to explore this area in an explicit and unembarrassed way. They are very readable and can help to allay a lot of anxieties about sexual feelings and behaviour.

Friday's Child
by Carol Lee
published by Thorsons Publishing Group

A personal account of sex education for teenagers in schools which is readable and particularly sensitive about the neglected male angle.

4

BOOKS ABOUT BECOMING AN ADULT

Everygirls' Lifeguide
by Miriam Stoppard
published by Dorling Kindersley.

This book is informal and chatty and deals with many aspects of growing up, both physically and psychologically. It is well illustrated and easy to read. Its main fault is that it tries to cover too many areas at once, and we think that some of them are treated rather superficially, but it would do as an introduction.

A Woman in Your Own Right.
by Anne Dickson
published by Quartet Books

This is a clearly written, informative book looking at ways in which one can become more assertive by developing clear and direct ways of communicating. Particular areas addressed are saying "no", handling criticism, managing the expression of anger, sexuality and assertiveness, and how body language conveys feelings.
If you are male, you can read this book with advantage. It will tell you how many women feel and it may also help you to define yourself better.

The Blind Side of Eden
by Carol Lee
published by Bloomsbury

This is a book about men and women written by a woman. It is perceptive, clear and uncompromising. It can help many of us get a firm, more accurate view of ourselves through such processes as telling us how others see us. Read the last page first and then be prepared to put your feet up.

BOOKS ON SEXUAL ABUSE

As we mentioned in the text, sexual abuse has sometimes been experienced by people suffering from anorexia. Because this is a subject which is especially difficult to approach, we are including some books which might help you in thinking about it, and eventually talking about it.

I Know why the Caged Bird Sings
by Maya Angelou
published by Virago

If I Should Die Before I Wake
by Michelle Morris
published by Black Swan

These two books are written by people who have personally experienced sexual abuse.

A Girl like Abby.
by Hadley Irwin
published by Plus Fiction.

This book is a novel about sexual abuse and dealing with the experience.

Too Close Encounters and What to Do About Them.
by Rosemary Stones
published by Piccadilly Press.

This is a book about how to keep yourself safe and what to do if you find yourself in a dangerous or uncomfortable situation. It is easy to read and very practical in its approach.

4

BOOKS TO HELP WITH SOME OTHER PROBLEMS AND DIFFICULTIES ALSO ASSOCIATED WITH ANOREXIA NERVOSA

Human Agression.
by Anthony Storr
published by Penguin.

This book sets out to explain why anger and aggression evolved, and their value in many situations. It describes what happens to people when they are angry, and goes on to discuss how people are affected by anger when they can't express it.
It is a rather technical book, but we wanted to include something about this area of emotional experience because it's something anorectics usually have a lot of difficulty with. It is quite easy reading, and not long, so even if you find it hard to see yourself in the descriptions, give it a try.

Depression. The way out of your prison.
by Dorothy Rowe
published by Routledge & Kegan Paul

At some weights you may be spared depression, but as you gain weight or come out of anorexia nervosa you are certain to experience new feelings of hopelessness and helplessness. This can be frightening and it is likely that neither you nor your family have the skills to deal with such an episode. This book will help you recognise what is happening to you and what you can do about it. The book may also be useful to parents who are experiencing depression - as you begin to recover. If you feel that they are being helped then you can go on recovering.

104

USEFUL FICTION

There are very many novels written about relationships and feelings with which you might be able to identify and which you might find it helpful to read. We give just an introductory selection below.

The Secret Diary of Adrian Mole Aged 13 3/4
by Sue Townsend
published by Methuen

The Death of the Heart
by Elizabeth Bowen
published by Virago.

The Summer After the Funeral
by Jane Gardam
published by Penguin.

The Rainbow
by D.H. Lawrence
published by Penguin.

The Catcher in the Rye
by J.D. Salinger
published by Penguin

4